Puffin Books

MICE MATHS

If one mouse has 4 legs,
how many legs do 5 mice have?

If you can't work this out without seeing the mice,
then this book of number puzzles will certainly
help you! There are mice on almost every page to
help you learn more about shape, number and
measurement. You'll also learn to juggle with
numbers and sums, find your way through
mathematical mazes, work out how to share a pie
between lots of mice and find out just why the
fat cat gets fatter and fatter.
All you'll need is a pencil, a ruler, a calculator
(for some puzzles) and maybe a rubber, and
you're ready for action.

Rose Griffiths is a maths teacher who firmly
believes that maths can be easy and fun! She has
written several books on maths, including four
activity books for Puffin. She lives in Leicester
with her husband and seven children.

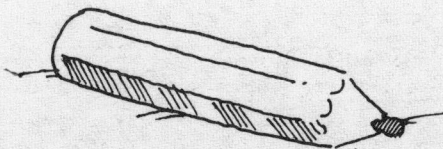

Also by Rose Griffiths

THE PUFFIN CALCULATOR BOOK
THE PUFFIN TIMES TABLES BOOK

MICE MATHS

Number and shape puzzles

Rose Griffiths

Illustrated by
Heather Clarke

PUFFIN BOOKS

PUFFIN BOOKS

Published by the Penguin Group
Penguin Books Ltd, 27 Wrights Lane, London W8 5TZ, England
Viking Penguin, a division of Penguin Books USA Inc.,
375 Hudson Street, New York, New York 10014, USA
Penguin Books Australia Ltd, Ringwood, Victoria, Australia
Penguin Books Canada Ltd, 2801 John Street, Markham, Ontario, Canada L3R 1B4
Penguin Books (NZ) Ltd, 182–190 Wairau Road, Auckland 10, New Zealand

Penguin Books Ltd, Registered Offices: Harmondsworth, Middlesex, England

First published 1991
3 5 7 9 10 8 6 4 2

Text copyright © Rose Griffiths, 1991
Illustrations copyright © Heather Clarke, 1991
All rights reserved

The moral right of the author has been asserted

Printed in England by Clays Ltd, St Ives plc
Filmset in Univers Medium

MICE MATHS

I asked 15 mice what they liked best in maths.

We put them all in this book!

Adding and taking away

Times tables and dividing

"Missing number" puzzles

Block graphs

Number patterns

Halves and quarters

Measuring

Drawing shapes

Telling the time

Codes

Mazes

Spotting odd and even numbers

Using a calculator

Following directions

Problems

EAST

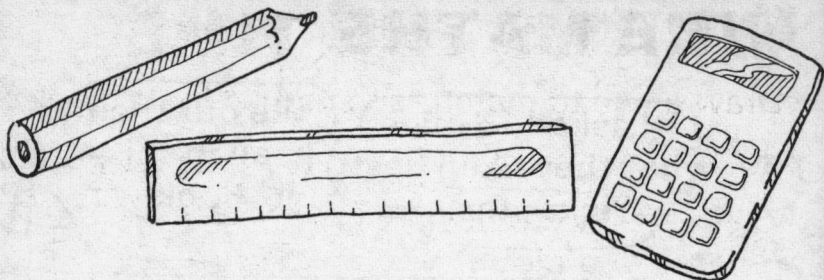

You will need a pencil or pen,
and a small ruler and a calculator
for some pages.

I like pencil best!
You can rub out
your mistakes.

ANSWERS are on pages 88 to 94.
Ask a grown-up to help you
if you get something wrong and
you can't work out why.

Have
fun!

WHAT'S THE TIME?

Draw a line to match each mouse to its clock.

1 My clock says 5 o'clock

2 My clock says 8 o'clock

3 My clock says 3 o'clock

4 My clock says 12 o'clock

5 My clock says 6 o'clock

SHORT STORIES

1 One mouse has 4 legs. How many legs do 5 mice have?

.... legs.

2  I saw 13 birds in a tree. Then 7 flew away. How many were left?

.... birds.

3 I fell asleep at 8 o'clock in the morning, and slept for 3 hours. What time did I wake up?

.... o'clock.

4  I ate 4 flies then I ate 8 more. How many did I eat altogether?

.... flies.

(5) I found 20 berries.
I ate 7, then 9 more,
then 1 more.
How many were left?

.... berries.

(6) I was born on June 1st 1987.
How old was I in June 1990?

.... years old.

(7) Spiders have 8 legs.
Flies have 6 legs.
How many legs do 3 spiders
and 2 flies have?

.... legs altogether.

(8) We had 32 berries to
share equally between us.
How many did each of
us get?

.... berries.

9

MICE MAZES

I've drawn a path through this maze.

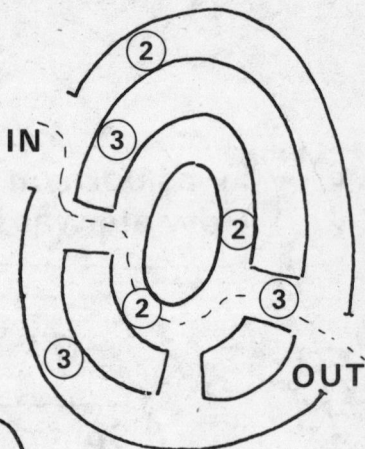

IN

(2)

(3)

(2)

(2) (3)

(3)

OUT

It was my 1st try. I scored ⟨5⟩ penalty points . . . . (2) + (3)

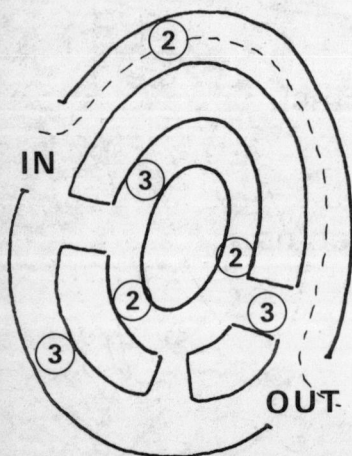

Here's my 2nd try. I did better this time. Only ⟨2⟩ penalty points.

(2)

IN

(3)

(2)

(2) (3)

(3)

OUT

help!

10

Try two paths through this maze.
Add up your penalty points.

OUT

IN

CALCULATORS

There is something unusual about one of these calculators.

Look at another calculator to help you.

Which calculator is strange, (A) or (B)? . . . .

MISSING NUMBERS

What goes in the boxes?
Use a calculator to
help you find out.

$20 + 13 =$ ☐

☐ $- 20 = 13$

☐ $- 13 = 20$

$42 - 18 =$ ☐

☐ $+ 18 = 42$

$42 -$ ☐ $= 18$

$100 - 2 =$ ☐

☐ $+ 2 = 100$

$100 -$ ☐ $= 2$

$15 + 45 =$ ☐

☐ $- 15 = 45$

☐ $- 45 = 15$

13

TABLES RACE ①

Answer as many of these as you can in 3 minutes.

Ask someone to time you.

① 3 × 4 =

② 7 × 1 =

③ 4 × 6 =

④ 5 × 3 =

⑤ 0 × 4 =

⑥ 4 × 4 =

⑦ 3 × 3 =

⑧ 7 × 2 =

⑨ 2 × 1 =

⑩ 1 × 9 =

⑪ 6 × 3 =

⑫ 0 × 0 =

⑬ 6 × 1 =

⑭ 2 × 5 =

⑮ 8 × 2 =

⑯ 5 × 5 =

⑰ 0 × 2 =

⑱ 1 × 1 =

⑲ 2 × 6 =

⑳ 2 × 2 =

Check your answers on page 88.

SCORE

....

14

MOUSE-CYCLES

There are 5 mice on bikes.
Each mouse has 4 legs, 2 ears, 2 eyes,
one tail and 10 whiskers.
Each bike has 2 wheels.

**How many ears
are there
altogether?**

....

**How many tails
are there
altogether?**

....

**How many legs
are there
altogether?**

....

**How many whiskers
are there
altogether?**

....

**How many wheels
are there
altogether?**

....

**How many eyes
are there
altogether?**

....

SANDWICHES

I've been making peanut-butter sandwiches.

And I've been cutting the sandwiches in half.

No, you haven't! Your pieces are *not* the same size. They are not equal. So they are *not* halves.

Help Tom Mouse check the sandwiches.
The pieces must be equal.

Has he cut these in half?
Write "Yes" or "No" for each one.

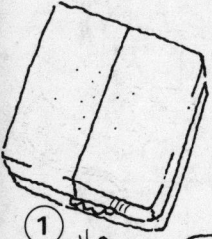

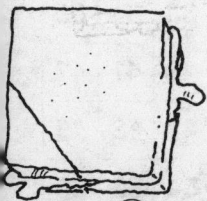

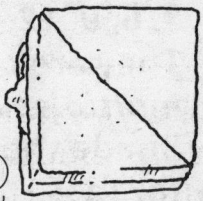

yes

THREES PATTERNS

We're holding up every third number.

I've started to shade in every third number on this grid.

I've shaded 3, 6, 9, 12, 15 . . . They are called *multiples of 3.* Shade the rest for me!

1	2	3	4	5	6	7
8	9	10	11	12	13	14
15	16	17	18	19	20	21
22	23	24	25	26	27	28
29	30	31	32	33	34	35
36	37	38	39	40	41	42
43	44	45	46	47	48	49
50	51	52	53	54	55	56
57	58	59	60	61	62	63

Now try these grids.

Shade in every third number on each one.
3, 6, 9, 12 . . .

1	2	3	4	5	6	7	8	9
10	11	12	13	14	15	16	17	18
19	20	21	22	23	24	25	26	27
28	29	30	31	32	33	34	35	36
37	38	39	40	41	42	43	44	45
46	47	48	49	50	51	52	53	54
55	56	57	58	59	60	61	62	63

1	2	3	4	5	6
7	8	9	10	11	12
13	14	15	16	17	18
19	20	21	22	23	24
25	26	27	28	29	30
31	32	33	34	35	36
37	38	39	40	41	42
43	44	45	46	47	48
49	50	51	52	53	54
55	56	57	58	59	60

1	2	3	4	5	6	7	8
9	10	11	12	13	14	15	16
17	18	19	20	21	22	23	24
25	26	27	28	29	30	31	32
33	34	35	36	37	38	39	40
41	42	43	44	45	46	47	48
49	50	51	52	53	54	55	56
57	58	59	60	61	62	63	64

DOTTY FROG

My friend Frog is hiding here!
Join the dots, to find her.

Start with 0, then join to 2, 4, 6 and
so on. All the numbers are *even*
numbers.

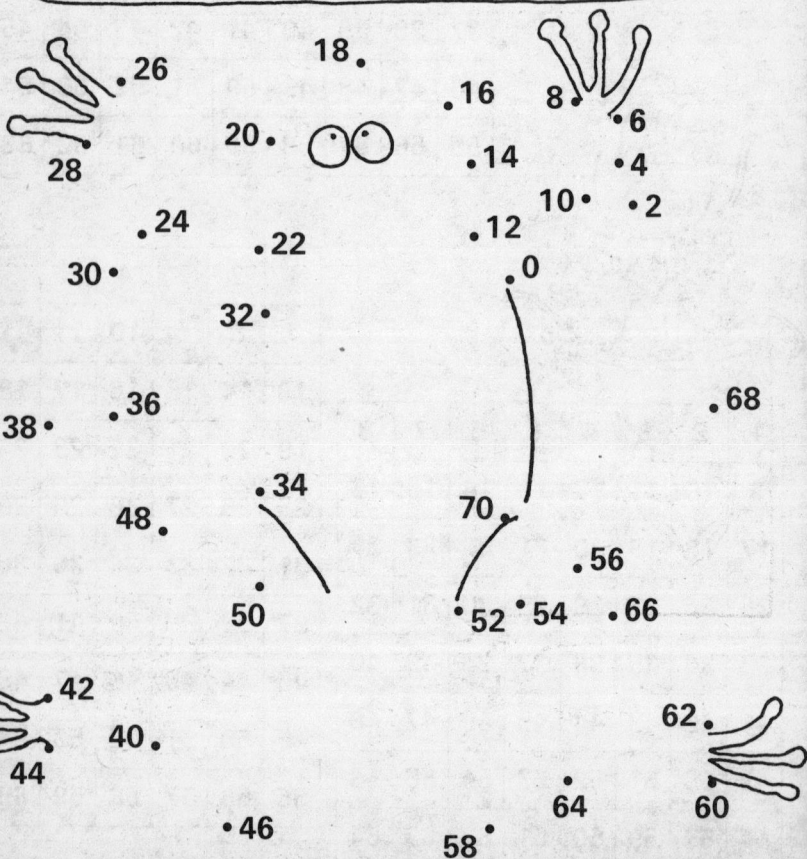

26
18
16
8
6
20
14
4
28
10
2
24
12
30
22
0
32
36
68
38
34
48
70
50
56
52 54 66
42
40
62
44
60
46
64
58

FLOWER BEDS

Three mice played in the park.
Each mouse ran once round a flower bed.

Which mouse ran the furthest? ....

WHICH DAY?

Each of these mice was born on a different day of the week.

Monday's mouse is full of cheese,
Tuesday's mouse likes eating peas.
Wednesday's mouse can run so fast,
Thursday's mouse is always last!
Friday's mouse is very shy,
Saturday's mouse can climb up high.
And Sunday's mouse is having a rest,
Warm and dry in his paper nest.

Can you work out which day each mouse was born on?

Flo was born on..

Raphael was born on ....

Emily was born on..

Tony was born on ....

Rickon was born on...

Jane was born on...

Claire was born on ....

ADD WITH TENS

Try these sums

(1)
```
  6
+4
___
```

(2)
```
  3
+8
___
```

(3)
```
  9
+1
___
```

(4)
```
  3
+6
___
```

(5)
```
  8
+2
___
```

(6)
```
  7
+5
___
```

(7)
```
  7
+3
___
```

(8)
```
  2
+9
___
```

(9)
```
  4
+8
___
```

(10)
```
  5
+5
___
```

Five of the sums added up to 10. Write them here:

I look for tens, to help me add up.

```
  14
   3
+  6
____
  23
```

4 and 6 make ten, so I add them first. Then add 3, then another 10.

LOOK FOR TENS to help you do these sums

These make 10

(11)
```
   8
  12
+ 17
_____
```

(12)
```
  21
  16
+  4
_____
```

(13)
```
  33
  33
+  7
_____
```

(14)
```
   5
  13
+ 25
_____
```

(15)
```
  11
  24
+  9
_____
```

(16)
```
   8
  32
+ 20
_____
```

(17)
```
   9
  49
+  1
_____
```

(18)
```
  24
   8
+  6
_____
```

(19)
```
  51
   5
+  5
_____
```

(20)
```
   4
   9
+  6
_____
```

Have you guessed what sort of snake I am?

(21) $4 + 2 + 6 + 8 + 3 =$

(22) $7 + 7 + 3 + 3 =$

I'm an adder!

TRUE OR FALSE?

A triangle is a shape with 3 straight sides.

True!

Write TRUE or FALSE for each of these:

1. This is a triangle.

....

2. This is a triangle.

....

3. This is a triangle.

....

4. This is a triangle.

....

A rectangle is a shape with 4 right angles and 4 straight sides.

True!

Write TRUE or FALSE for these:

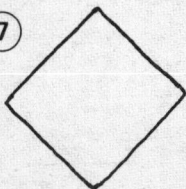

⑤ This is a rectangle.

⑥ This is a rectangle.

⑦ This is a rectangle.

⑧ This is a rectangle.

FISHY TAILS

Join numbers which add up to 10 to make tails for the fish.

Use a pencil and a ruler.

9 + 1 = 10, so I've joined 9 to 1.

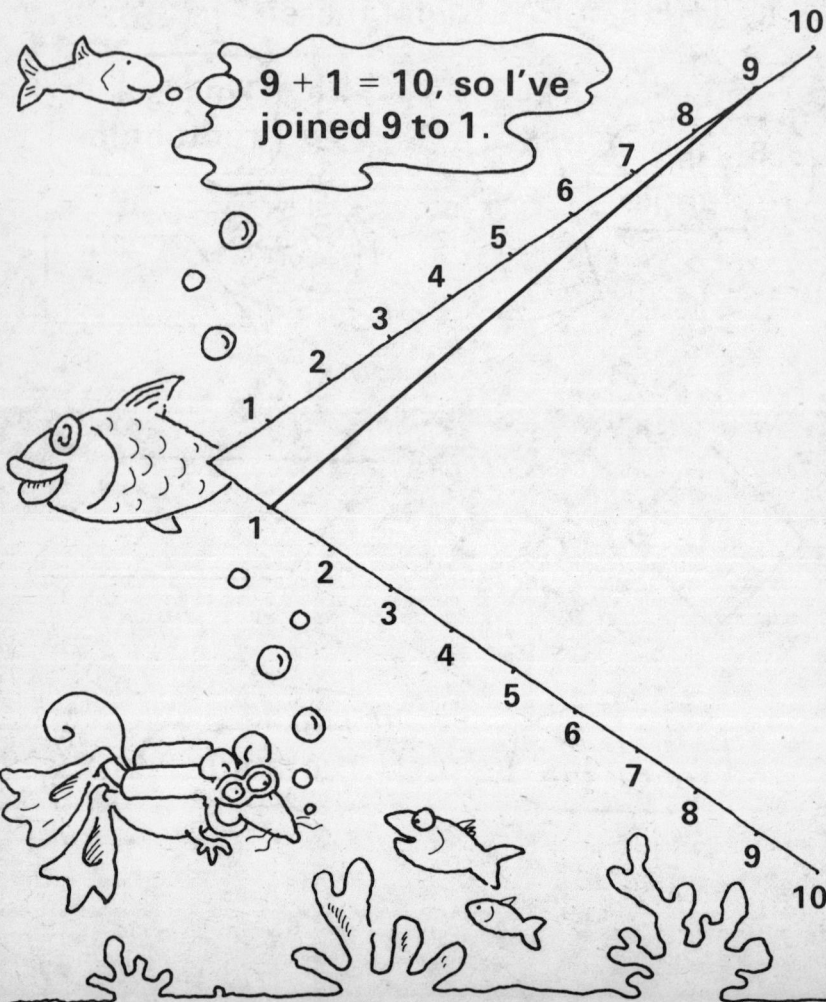

10

9

8

7

6

5

4

3

2

1

1

2

3

4

5

6

7

8

9

10

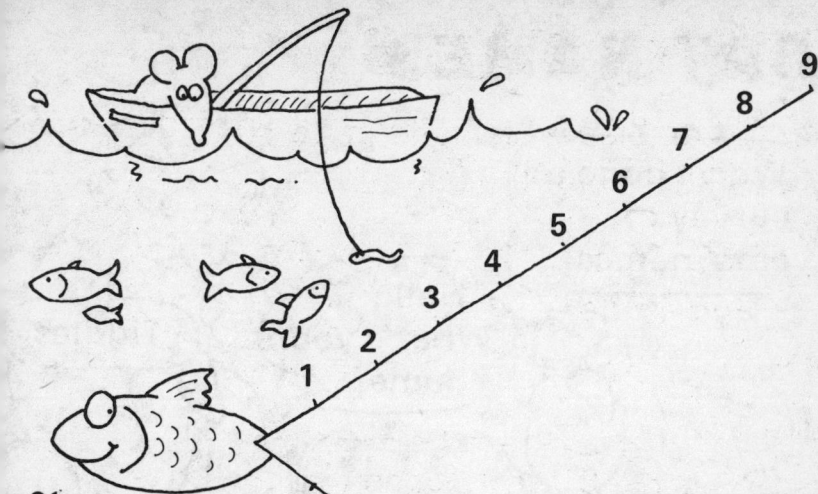

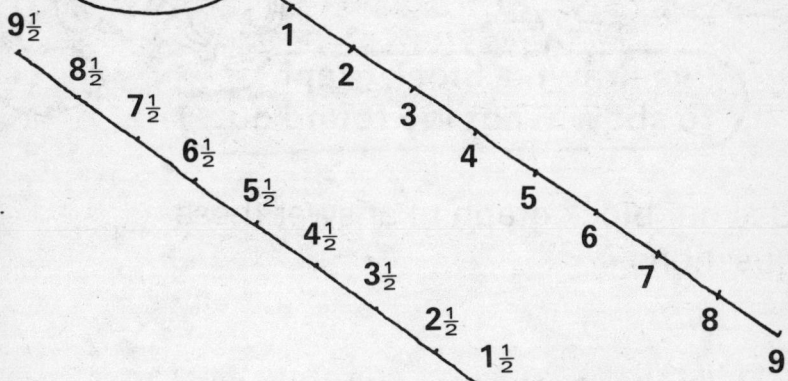

CAT NAMES

We've done a survey of cats' names.

Hello. What's your name?

Tiddles

I've drawn a block graph to show what we found out.

Use our block graph to answer these questions.

(1) Which was the most popular cat's name? ....

(2) How many cats were called Smokey? ....

(3) How many cats were called Kitty? ....

(4) How many cats were called Ginger? ....

(5) How many cats did we ask altogether? ....

Number of Cats

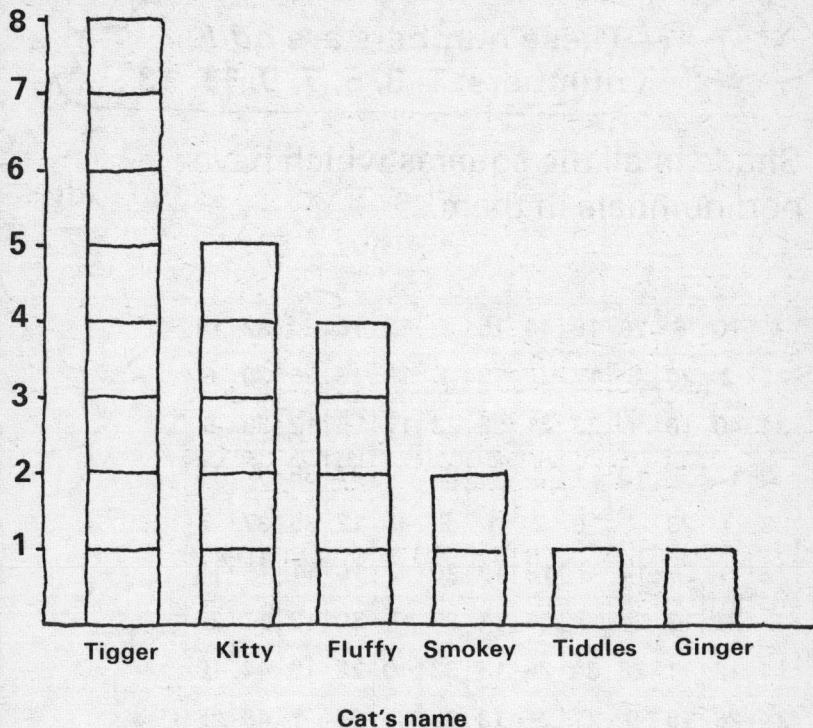

Bar chart showing number of cats by name:
- Tigger: 8
- Kitty: 5
- Fluffy: 4
- Smokey: 2
- Tiddles: 1
- Ginger: 1

Cat's name

ODD OWL

These numbers are *odd* numbers: 1, 3, 5, 7, 9, 11, 13 . . .

Shade in all the squares which have odd numbers in them.

4	10	6	20	18	44	15	2	12	16	24	32	14
22	2	24	8	17	3	13	1	19	18	36	30	6
34	40	16	1	23	21	25	23	17	15	12	38	8
2	12	5	19	21	3	5	29	5	27	39	4	16
28	7	23	4	10	2	1	8	6	12	35	37	8
22	9	7	14	3	18	19	20	5	16	11	15	18
6	21	13	24	9	36	11	38	7	30	13	17	20
14	18	11	28	34	26	15	32	40	22	15	44	10
24	26	15	9	27	9	13	33	31	25	7	48	26
16	32	29	7	13	17		19	11	21	13	2	42
14	28	5	41	29	11	41	21	23	9	11	46	50
30	4	27	31	31	19	39	45	9	49	23	4	10
16	12	13	17	43	21	7	25	19	39	17	20	24
18	6	25	3	35	41	37	47	27	37	35	8	22
34	2	8	5	1	3	33	31	1	29	10	14	6
18	16	42	10	7			42	18	3		12	38
36	12	40			38	36	34			32	22	40
20	22			24	26	28			30	14	20	24

I'm going!

LONG MAZE

Draw a path
through the maze.

Score penalty points
every time you go
over a circle.

Add up your total:

Try another path.
Try to get *less*
penalty points.

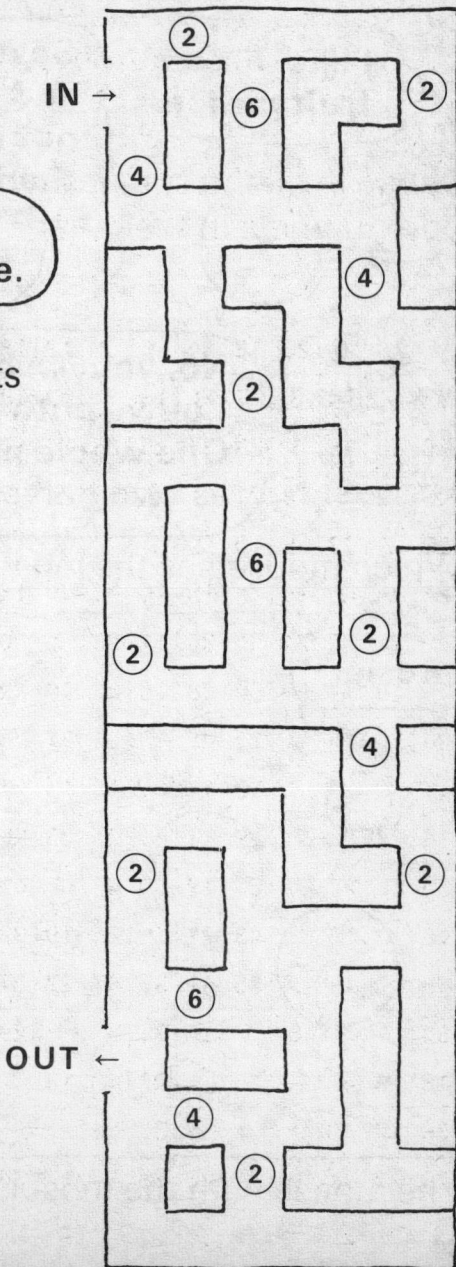

IN →

OUT ←

WHO HAS MOST?

I like fruit pies.

So do I – and I've got more than you!

No, you *haven't* got more. You've both got the same. One whole pie is the same as two halves of pie.

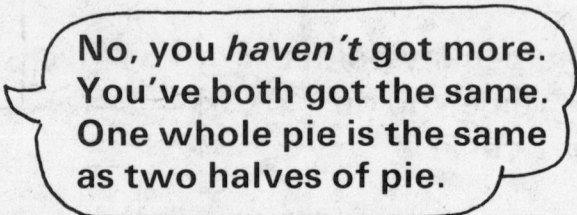

Which mouse has the most pie?

I'm Rosie.

I'm Robert.

The mouse with the most is ....

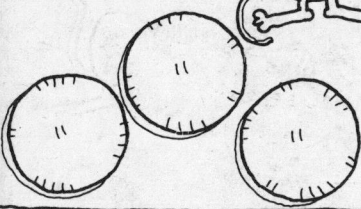 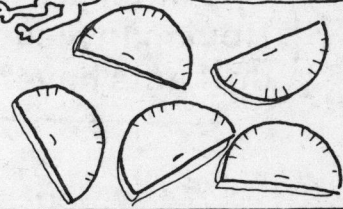

The mouse with the most is ....

The mouse with the most is ....

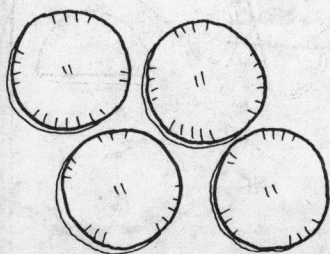 

The mouse with the most is ....

MORE STORIES

1 One ant has 6 legs.
How many legs
do 4 ants have?

.... legs.

2 I slept from 9 o'clock in the
morning until 1 o'clock in
the afternoon.
How long was I asleep?

.... hours.

3 I'm Shaun.
I was born in 1985.

I'm Kelly.
I was born in 1986.

Who is oldest? ....

4

We found 21 biscuits.
We shared them equally.
How many biscuits did
each of us get?

.... biscuits each.

5

I'm Owen.
I'm 10 years old.

I'm Andy.
I'm 6 years old.

How much older than Andy is Owen?
.... years older.

6

I had 15 pieces of apple.
I ate 7.
How many were left?

.... pieces of apple.

HIDING

Help me find Emma Mouse.
She's hiding behind a
bush in the garden.

She has left us instructions.
For example, **N4** means "Go 4 steps North".

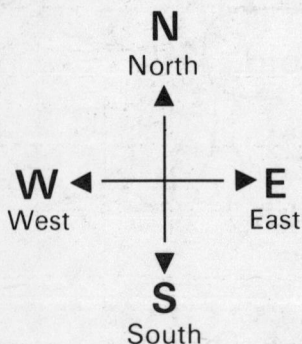

N
North

W ◄ ►E
West   East

S
South

This much
is one step.

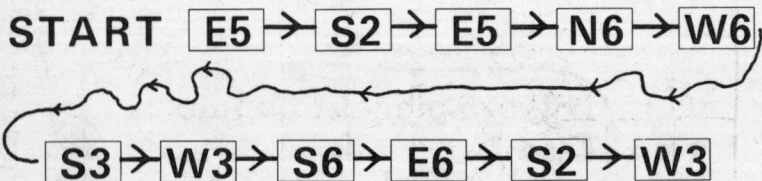

START E5 → S2 → E5 → N6 → W6

S3 → W3 → S6 → E6 → S2 → W3

Which bush is Emma Mouse behind?

START

1

2

3

4

5

6

39

WHAT COMES NEXT?

Write down the next
3 numbers for each
of these . . .

① 1 3 5 7 9

② 24 22 20 18

③ 7 14 21

④ 1 3

5

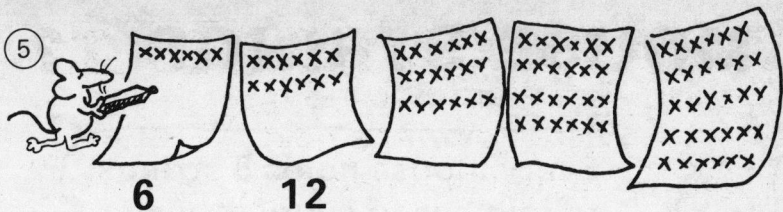

6   12

6

60   55   50

7

2 4 6 8 10 12 14

8

21   18   15

9

10   9   8

Answers are on page 90.

MOUSE STRINGS

Every mouse holds 5 strings, to join her to every other mouse on the circle.

Draw on all the strings for all the mice.
Use a pencil and a ruler.

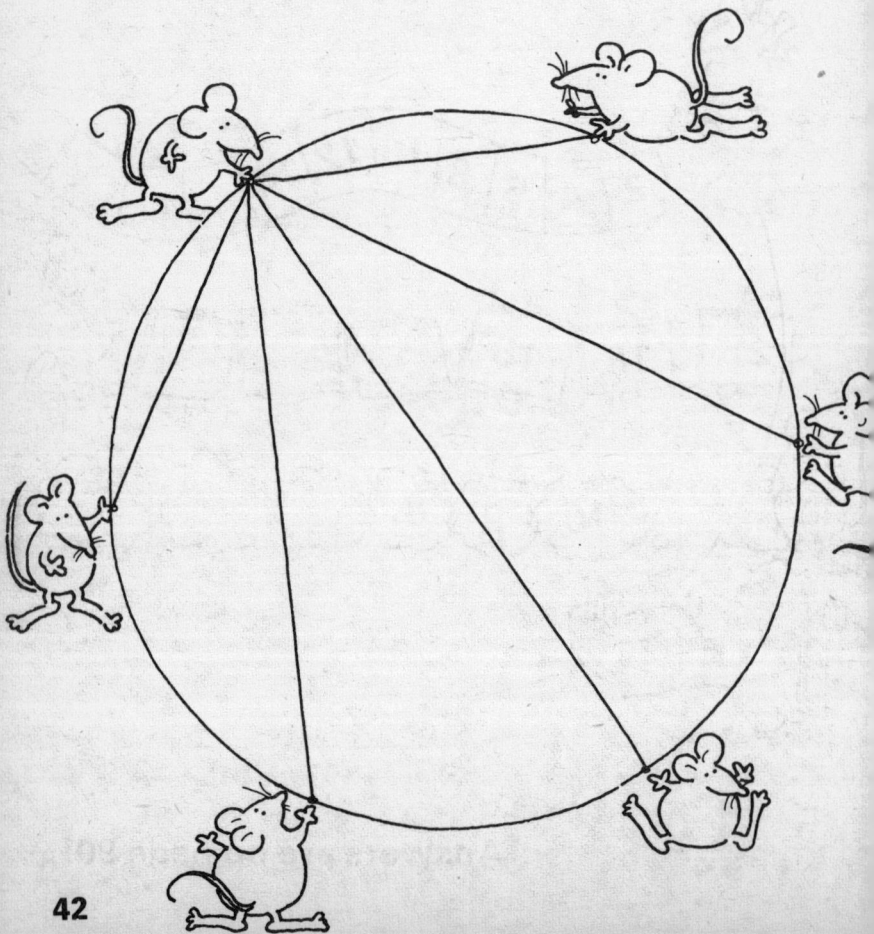

One mouse has gone home!
There are 5 mice now, and each
one holds 4 strings.

Draw on all the strings.

Colour in your patterns if you want to.

TABLES RACE ②

Answer as many of these as you can in 3 minutes.

Ask someone to time you.

①	$2 \times 6 =$	⑪	$4 \times 2 =$
②	$2 \times 3 =$	⑫	$7 \times 5 =$
③	$3 \times 10 =$	⑬	$0 \times 7 =$
④	$4 \times 3 =$	⑭	$5 \times 4 =$
⑤	$0 \times 9 =$	⑮	$0 \times 3 =$
⑥	$6 \times 6 =$	⑯	$9 \times 2 =$
⑦	$1 \times 0 =$	⑰	$10 \times 8 =$
⑧	$4 \times 10 =$	⑱	$3 \times 1 =$
⑨	$6 \times 5 =$	⑲	$0 \times 4 =$
⑩	$10 \times 1 =$	⑳	$5 \times 7 =$

SCORE

....

Check your answers on page 90.

CLOCK SHOP

The clocks in this shop should all say 4 o'clock.

Help the mice decide which clocks are *right*, and which clocks are *wrong*.

1) **Right**

4)

2)

3)

5)

6)

7)

MOUSE NESTS

I asked 16 mice what they liked best to make their nests from.

Paper

Leaves

Hay

Cloth

Paper

Cloth

Paper

Cloth

Cloth

Cloth

Hay

Leaves

Paper

Cloth

Cloth

Hay

How many mice liked paper best? ....

How many mice liked leaves best? ....

How many mice liked hay best? ....

How many mice liked cloth best? ....

I've started to draw a block graph. Can you finish it for me?

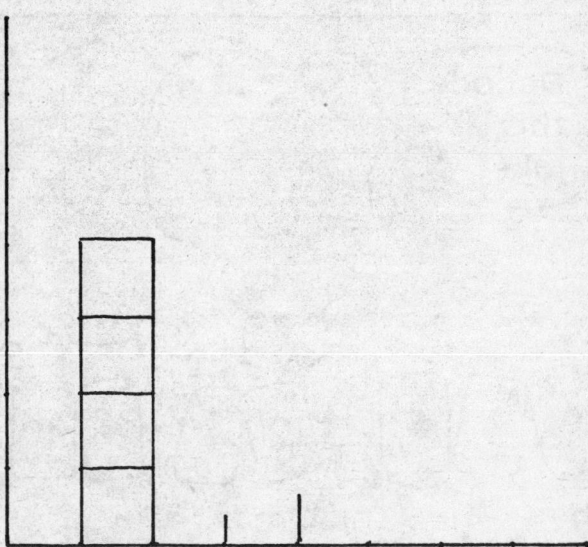

What did *most* mice like the best to make their nests from? ....

CARD CODE

Each card stands for a letter.

A B C D E F G H I J K L M

N O P Q R S T U V W X Y Z

Decode this joke!

Wh

_ _

_ _

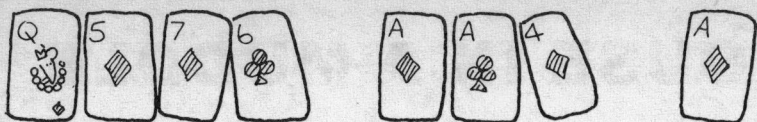

- -

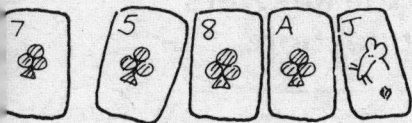

- - - - - - - - - - - ?

- -

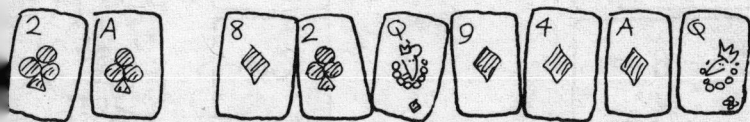

- -

MOUSE IN A MUDDLE

The baby mice have mixed up the answers to all my questions.

Draw a line from each question to the right answer.

4 × 6 =	6
6 × 5 =	2
6 × 6 =	3
12 ÷ 6 =	30
6 × 0 =	24
18 ÷ 6 =	0
6 × 1 =	36

What muddle!

DOT TO DOT

My friend Chicken is hiding here!
Join the dots, to find her.

Start with 0, and join all the *even*
numbers, 2, 4, 6 and so on.
Then join the *odd* numbers, 1, 3, 5 . . .

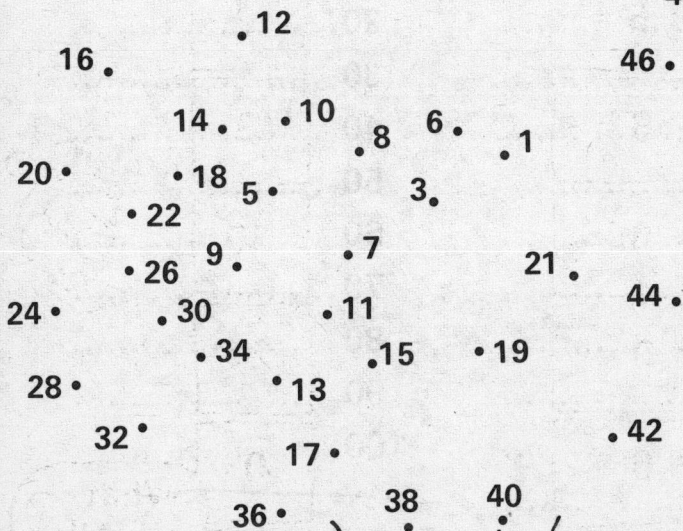

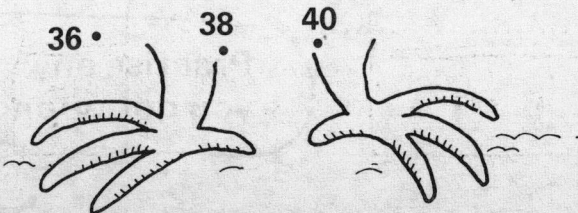

.2

4.

.0

48.

.12

16.

.10

14.

46.

.8   6.

.1

20.

.18   5.

3.

.22

.26   9.

.7

21.

44.

24.

.30

.11

.34

.15   .19

28.

.13

32.

.42

17.

36.   38.   40.

CHECK YOUR SPELLING

Can you spell all these numbers?

Check your answers on page 91.

1	....	20	....
2	....	30	....
3	....	40	....
4	....	50	....
5	....	60	....
6	....	70	....
7	....	80	....
8	....	90	....
9	....	100	....
10	....		

Practise any you got wrong!

CROSSWORD

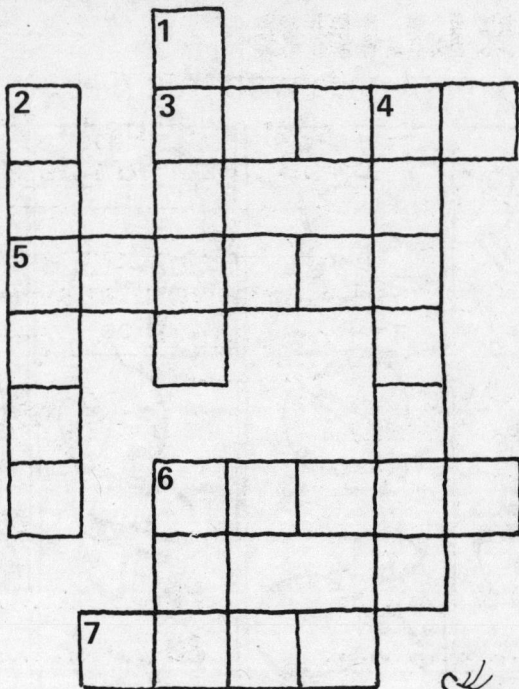

CLUES ACROSS:
3. Four add four.
5. Eighteen take away seven.
6. Eight take away five.
7. Eleven take away seven.

CLUES DOWN:
1. Four add three.
2. Thirty take away ten.
4. Eighty add twenty.
6. One add one.

PIE QUESTIONS

Here are more mice with fruit pies.

Bella

Sam

Alice

Patrick

I've only got one pie.

1. Which mouse has $3\frac{1}{2}$ pies? ....

2. Which mouse has cut her pies into quarters? ....

3. Which mouse has $2\frac{1}{2}$ pies? ....

4. Which mouse has the most pies? ....

These mice have cut their pies into quarters.

These mice have cut their pies into halves.

5. Which mouse has the same amount
   of pie as Robin? Is it Lily or Jamie?

   ....

6. Which mouse has the same amount
   of pie as Rachel? Is it Lily or Jamie?

   ....

NIBBLED NUMBERS

The sums on this page all have a number missing!

Amy Mouse has eaten her favourite number!

Can you work out what it is?
Check with a calculator if you want to.

$$
\begin{array}{r}
25 \\
+29 \\
+ \\
\hline
58
\end{array}
$$

$13 \times = 52$

$100 \div 25 = $

$90 - = 86$

Amy Mouse's nibbled number is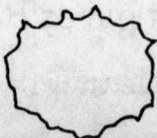

Now Jo Mouse has eaten *his* favourite number!

Can you work out what it is?

$$\boxed{}\ \boxed{} + 1 = 100$$

$$\boxed{} \times \boxed{} = 81$$

$$10 - \boxed{} = 1$$

$$45 \div \boxed{} = 5$$

Jo Mouse's nibbled number is

TICK OR CROSS

I've been practising my tables.
I don't think I've got them all right.

Put a √ or × for each of my answers.

Three Times Table	Five Times Table
0 × 3 = 0 √	0 × 5 = 0
1 × 3 = 3 √	1 × 5 = 5
2 × 3 = 8 ×	2 × 5 = 12
3 × 3 = 9	3 × 5 = 15
4 × 3 = 12	4 × 5 = 20
5 × 3 = 15	5 × 5 = 25
6 × 3 = 19	6 × 5 = 36
7 × 3 = 21	7 × 5 = 37
8 × 3 = 24	8 × 5 = 40
9 × 3 = 28	9 × 5 = 45
10 × 3 = 30	10 × 5 = 50

How many did I get wrong? ....

SQUARE MAZE

IN

OUT

Draw a path
through the maze.

Score penalty points every time you go
over a circle. Add up your total:

Try another path.
Try to get *less* penalty points:

MORE SANDWICHES

Some of my sandwiches are cut into *halves*. Some of my sandwiches are cut into *quarters*.

Which are which?
Write *halves* or *quarters*.

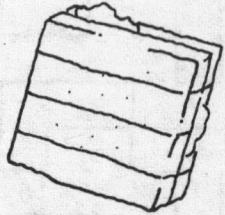

① ....   ② ....

③ ....   ④ ....

Can you draw another way of cutting my sandwiches into quarters?

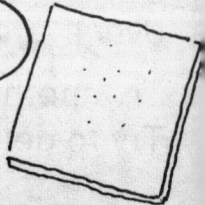

DOTTY MOUSE

Join the dots to find Mouse.
The numbers are all multiples of 3.

Start with 0, then 3, 6, 9, and
so on.

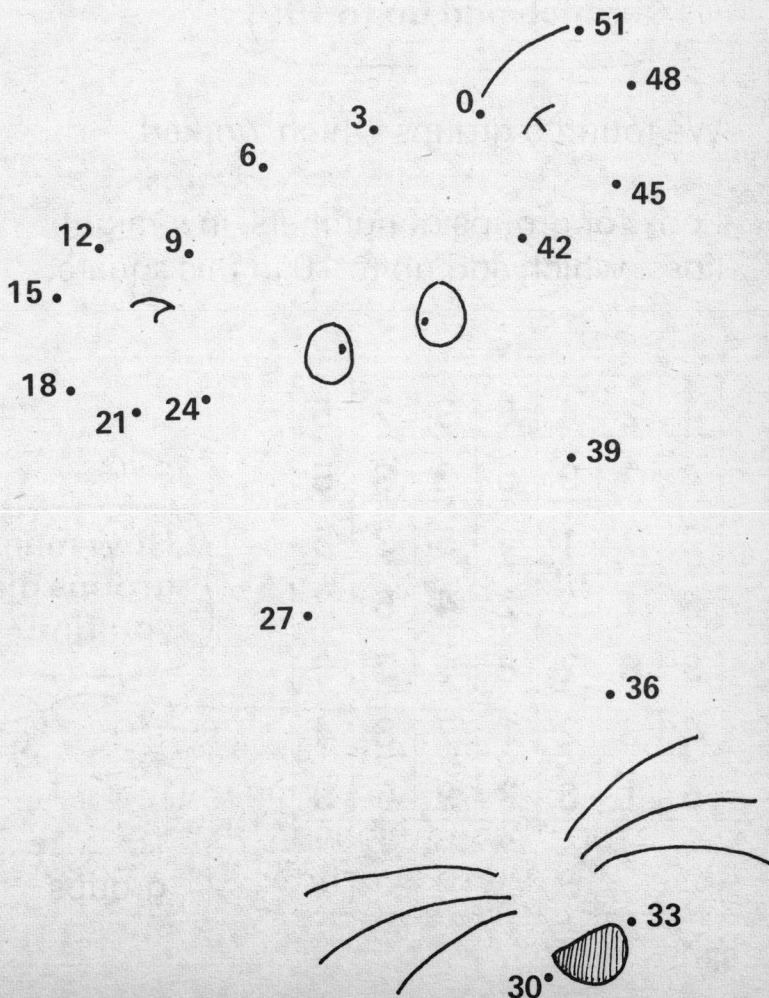

ADD-UPS

We've drawn round groups of numbers which add up to 10.

4	2	4	1
1	5	7	9
3	6	8	9
6	2	3	2

We found 5 groups which worked.

Look for groups of numbers, in straight lines, which add up to 10 in this square.

4	2	4	6	3	7	5
4	2	9	5	2	8	5
2	7	1	4	5	3	6
8	1	3	2	4	5	3
9	8	2	6	1	7	9
4	3	2	1	7	8	4
5	1	6	3	9	6	9

How many groups did you find?

....
groups.

Find groups which add up to 11 in this square.

5	6	6	1	5	9	10
3	4	2	7	8	2	9
8	1	4	1	6	2	6
3	8	4	3	5	3	6
10	5	9	7	2	7	2
1	5	2	4	3	4	8
9	1	5	10	1	6	7

How many groups of 11 did you find?

.... groups.

Find groups which add up to 12 in this square.

3	2	1	4	3	5
7	3	3	3	3	9
2	8	7	6	5	3
1	6	6	11	10	9
1	2	4	5	2	6
11	4	8	10	4	8

How many did you find?

.... groups.

FROG HOPS

I have been given a message. Someone has left some instructions.

For example, SE2 means, "Hop South East, 2 hops".

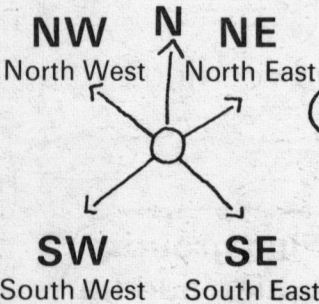

NW — North West
N
NE — North East

SW — South West
SE — South East

Dear Frog,
Come and visit me.
Follow these instructions.

START → SE3 → SW5 → SE2 → SW2

→ SE2 → NE3 → SE4 → SW4 → NW1

→ SW2 → SE3 → SW4

Does Frog visit Mouse or Bird? ....

START

DOTTY SHAPES

You need a pencil
and a ruler.
Join the dots,
1 → 2 → 3 → . . .

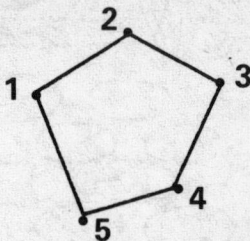

Some of the shapes have 5 sides.
They are called *pentagons*.

Some of the shapes have 6 sides.
They are called *hexagons*.

Write *pentagon* or *hexagon*
for each shape.

(A)

This is a

h. . . . .

66

(B) This is a ....

2.

1.
.3
.4

.5

(C) This is a ....

2.
.3

1.

.4

.5

(D) This is a ....

2.
.3

1.

.4

6.

.5

(E) This is a ....

2.
.3

1.

.4

.5

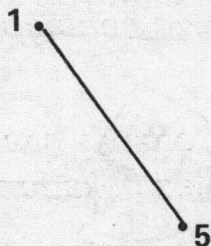

QUESTION MACHINE

This is our question machine.
We put in **8**, then
Katie Mouse turned the handle.

The machine gave us lots of different ways of making **8**.

8

2 + 6   3 + 5   4 × 2

8 × 1   4 + 4   1 + 7

2 × 4

Check that these all make 8.

Use a calculator if you want to.

We've put in 9 .
Make up some questions
for our machine!

1×9

Now we've put in 12 .
Make up some questions
for our machine.

$3 + 9$

SHADY SQUARES

The first question here is $17 - 15$
The answer is 2.
So I have shaded in the square
with number 2 in it.

Shade in the answers to the
other questions, to find out what
our friend is saying.

1	2	3	4	5
6	7	8	9	10
11	12	13	14	15
16	17	18	19	20
21	22	23	24	25

1	2	3	4	5
6	7	8	9	10
11	12	13	14	15
16	17	18	19	20
21	22	23	24	25

$17 - 15 = 2$ $9 + 13 =$
$2 + 6 + 9 =$ $2 \times 6 =$
$2 \times 7 =$ $23 - 10 =$
$21 - 12 =$ $11 + 8 =$
$8 + 16 =$ $20 - 13 =$
                  $19 - 15 =$

$18 - 15 =$ $12 \div 6 =$
$21 - 14 =$ $2 \times 2 =$
$7 \times 2 =$ $24 \div 2 =$
$8 + 9 =$ $4 \times 3 + 1 =$
$2 \times 11 =$ $17 + 6 =$
$2 \times 12 =$

————— !

1	2	3	4	5
6	7	8	9	10
11	12	13	14	15
16	17	18	19	20
21	22	23	24	25

$91 - 89 =$ $22 - 15 =$

$13 + 4 =$ $9 + 14 =$

$11 \times 2 =$ $6 \times 2 =$

$20 + 4 =$

1	2	3	4	5
6	7	8	9	10
11	12	13	14	15
16	17	18	19	20
21	22	23	24	25

$3 \times 3 =$ $35 - 28 =$

$21 - 4 =$ $7 + 6 =$

$9 \div 3 =$ $4 \times 1 =$

$9 + 5 =$ $8 + 14 =$

$10 \div 5 =$ $3 \times 4 =$

FAT CAT

When she wakes up each morning, this cat always weighs the same as 10 mice.

On Monday, she ate 2 mice for breakfast!

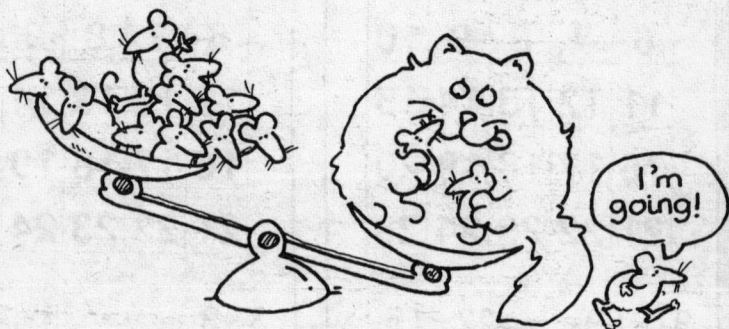

I'm going!

After breakfast, she weighed the same as 12 mice.

Is this safe?

How many mice did Fat Cat eat for
breakfast on these days?

**Remember: when she wakes up
each morning, she always weighs the
same as 10 mice.**

TUESDAY

I ate ...... mice
for
breakfast.

WEDNESDAY

I ate ...... mice
for
breakfast.

THURSDAY

I ate ...... mice
for
breakfast.

WASHING LINES

The numbers on each washing line all have something in common – except for one!

Colour in each odd-one-out.

a

30   18   50   20   40   60

b

2   6   4   10   7   12

74

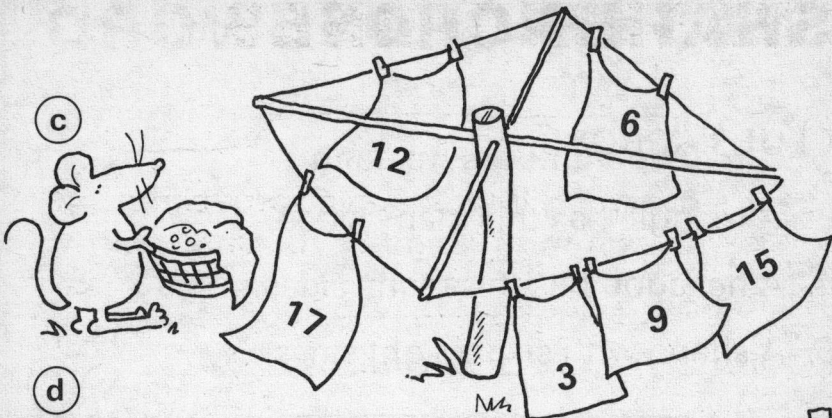

SHAPES CROSSWORD

CLUES ACROSS:

3. A triangle has this many sides.

4. A hexagon has this many sides.

6. A shape with six straight sides.

7. **This shape reminds me of a wheel on my bicycle.**

8. A square has this many sides – and so does a rectangle.

CLUES DOWN:

1. **This shape is a R _ _ _ _ _ _ _**

2. A special kind of rectangle, which has all its sides the same length.

3. A shape with three straight sides.

5. A shape with five straight sides.

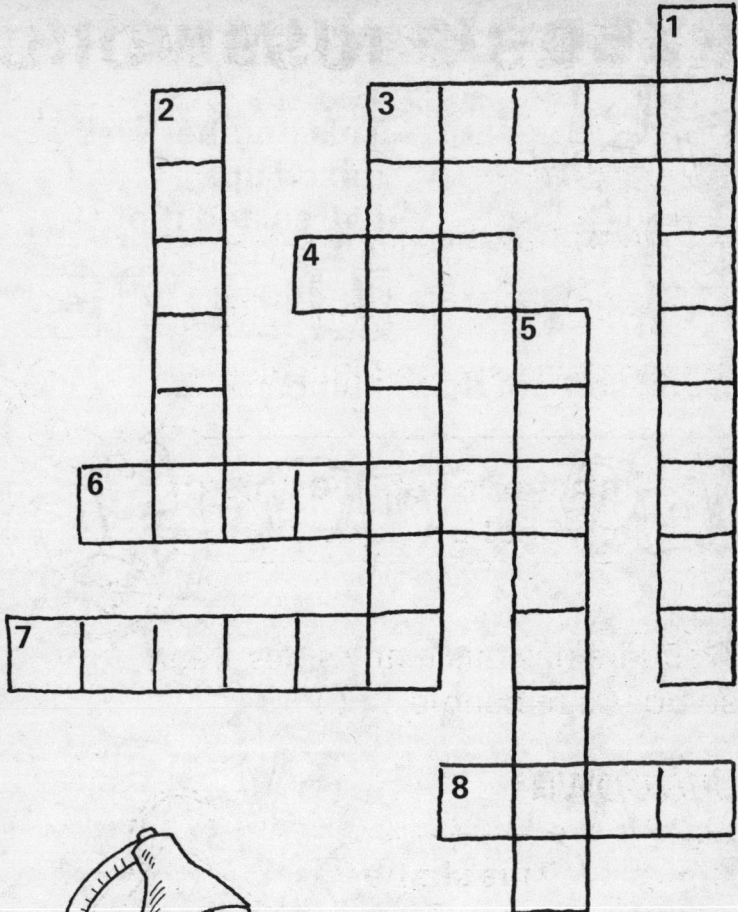

MIXED-UP NUMBERS

This number was
mixed up.
I've sorted it out!

Can you sort out these numbers?

....

....

....

....

....

....

GARDEN PATHS

These mice ran along paths in the garden.

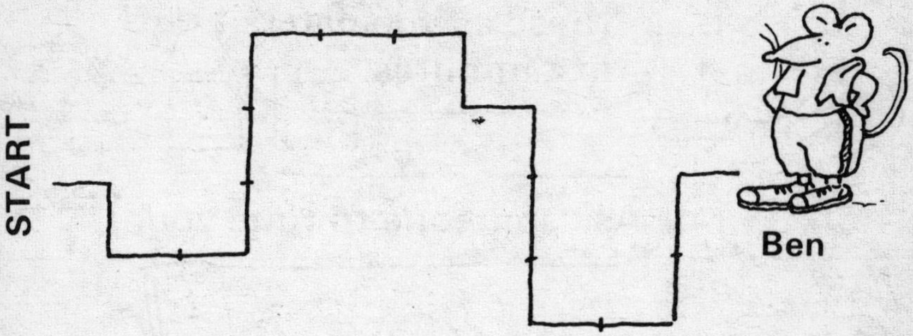

START

Ben

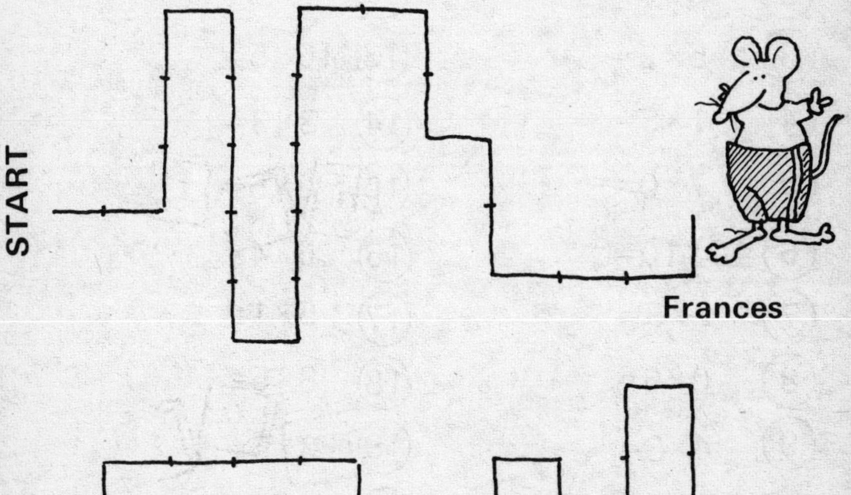

START

Frances

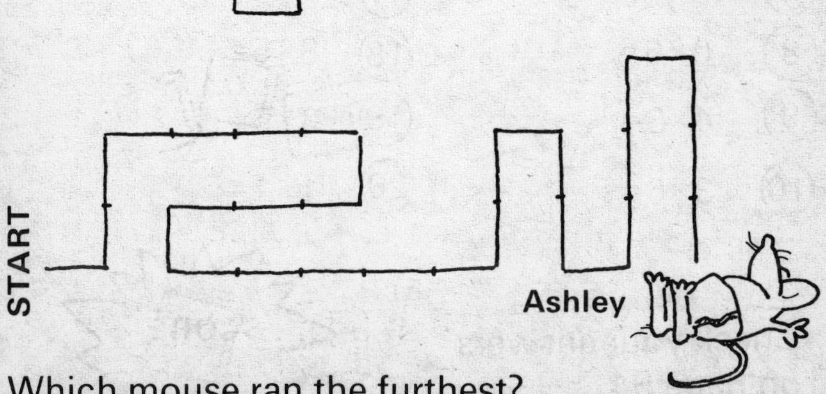

START

Ashley

Which mouse ran the furthest? ....

TABLES RACE ③

Answer as many of these as you can in 3 minutes.

Ask someone to time you.

① $2 \times 4 =$
② $5 \times 5 =$
③ $5 \times 2 =$
④ $1 \times 8 =$
⑤ $7 \times 0 =$
⑥ $10 \times 10 =$
⑦ $2 \times 9 =$
⑧ $0 \times 6 =$
⑨ $4 \times 3 =$
⑩ $3 \times 6 =$

⑪ $4 \times 4 =$
⑫ $7 \times 3 =$
⑬ $10 \times 5 =$
⑭ $3 \times 3 =$
⑮ $0 \times 5 =$
⑯ $6 \times 4 =$
⑰ $5 \times 1 =$
⑱ $8 \times 5 =$
⑲ $3 \times 5 =$
⑳ $1 \times 1 =$

Check your answers on page 94.

SCORE
....

80

SUM SEARCH

Find three numbers in a straight line
which make a sum. Use $+$ $-$ $\times$ or $\div$.

We've found 2 sums
to get you started!

$12 = 3 \times 4$

and $5 - 3 = 2$

2	2	3	5	1	5	6
4	1	2	3	5	3	2
3	10	6	4	5	9	4
4	15	8	7	10	3	3
12	5	4	20	13	7	8
6	3	2	5	7	12	3
2	8	4	3	6	5	11

PLAYGROUND

I like going to the playground.

Some days, I go *clockwise* around the playground.

It's called *clockwise* because it's the same way that the hands on a clock go round.

Some days, I go anti-clockwise around the playground.

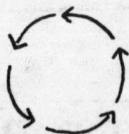

Which way did I go on these days: clockwise or anti-clockwise?

On Monday, I went on the rope, then the seesaw, then the slide.
I went ....

On Tuesday, I went on the swing, then the slide, then the rope.
I went ....

On Wednesday, I went on the seesaw, then the rope, then the slide.
I went ....

On Thursday, I went in the sandpit, then
  on the slide, then on the swing.
  I went ....

TIMES TABLES CODE

Write down the letter which goes with each answer to decode my joke!

A	B	C	D	E	F	G	H	I	J	K	L	M
0	1	4	6	8	9	10	12	14	15	16	18	20

N	O	P	Q	R	S	T	U	V	W	X	Y	Z
21	24	25	30	35	40	45	50	60	70	80	90	100

10×7 3×4 6×0 9×5 ' 5×8 5×9 2×6 2×4

W H _

2×3 2×7 3×3 1×9 2×4 5×7 4×2 3×7 2×2 4×2

_ _

1×1 2×4 5×9 10×7 2×4 4×2 3×7 0×4 7×3

_ _

4×2 2×9 2×4 5×5 6×2 0×2 3×7 5×9

10×0 7×3 2×3 0×9

1×1 2×7 8×5 2×2 5×10 2×7 5×9 ?

                                                 ?

9×10 4×6 5×10 2×2 8×0 3×7 5×9

2×3 2×7 5×5 0×5 3×7

2×4 3×6 2×4 5×5 2×6 4×0 7×3 9×5

7×2 3×7 9×10 6×4 5×10 5×7 5×9 4×2 0×1 !

                                                 !

CLIMBING FRAME

I'm building a climbing frame.

I used rectangles at first ....

but they wobble about and change shape!

Triangles are much stronger.

Finish drawing my climbing frame for me.

Join the dots to make triangles. Use a ruler!

DIVIDING

We had 20 marbles.
We shared them fairly
between us.

5 marbles
each.

I checked
on my calculator.
| 20 | ÷ | 4 | = | 5 |

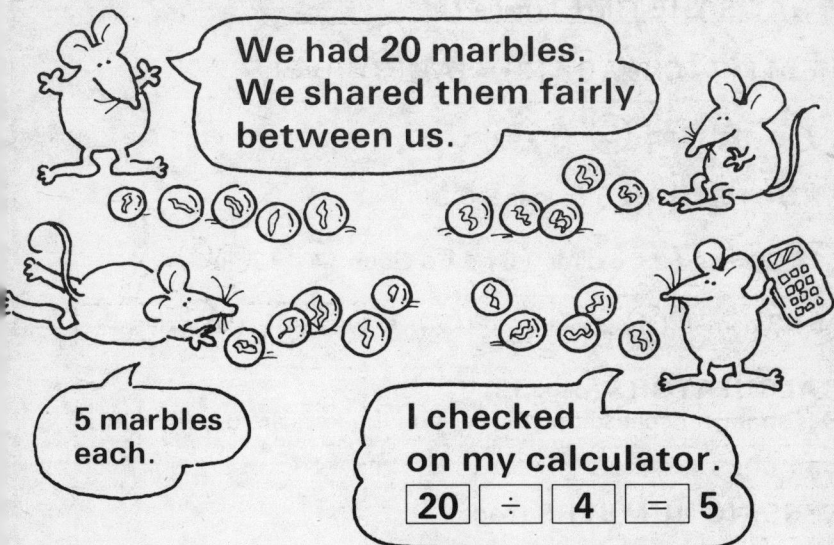

Work these out. Check them on a
calculator.

① If we had 16 marbles, how many would
we each get? .... | 16 | ÷ | 4 | = | ....

② If we had 4 marbles, how many would
we each get? .... | 4 | ÷ | 4 | = | ....

③ If we had 40 marbles, how many would
we each get? .... | 40 | ÷ | 4 | = | ....

④ If we had *no* marbles, how many would
we each get? .... | 0 | ÷ | 4 | = | ....

ANSWERS

WHAT'S THE TIME? (page 7)

Mouse (1) →Clock (C) , (2) → (A) , (3) → (E) ,

(4) → (D) , and (5) → (B) .

SHORT STORIES (pages 8 & 9)

(1) 20 legs (2) 6 birds (3) 11 o'clock (4) 12 flies

(5) 3 berries (6) 3 years old (7) 36 legs (8) 16 berries.

CALCULATORS (page 12)

B is strange, because the numbers on the keys are usually

```
789
456
123
```

MISSING NUMBERS (page 13)

20 + 13 = $\boxed{33}$ 42 − 18 = $\boxed{24}$
$\boxed{33}$ − 20 = 13 $\boxed{24}$ + 18 = 42
$\boxed{33}$ − 13 = 20   42 − $\boxed{24}$ = 18

100 − 2 = $\boxed{98}$ 15 + 45 = $\boxed{60}$
$\boxed{98}$ + 2 = 100 $\boxed{60}$ − 15 = 45
100 − $\boxed{98}$ = 2 $\boxed{60}$ − 45 = 15

TABLES RACE (1) (page 14)

(1) 12	(6) 16	(11) 18	(16) 25
(2) 7	(7) 9	(12) 0	(17) 0
(3) 24	(8) 14	(13) 6	(18) 1
(4) 15	(9) 2	(14) 10	(19) 12
(5) 0	(10) 9	(15) 16	(20) 4.

MOUSE-CYCLES (page 15)

10 ears, 5 tails, 20 legs, 50 whiskers, 10 wheels, and 10 eyes.

SANDWICHES (pages 16 & 17)

These four are Yes : 1, 4, 5, 8

The others are all No .

THREES PATTERNS (pages 18 & 19)

1	2	**3**	4	5	**6**	7
8	**9**	10	11	**12**	13	14
15	16	17	**18**	19	20	**21**
22	23	**24**	25	26	**27**	28
29	**30**	31	32	**33**	34	35
36	37	38	**39**	40	41	**42**
43	44	**45**	46	47	**48**	49
50	**51**	52	53	**54**	55	56
57	58	59	**60**	61	62	**63**

1	2	**3**	4	5	**6**	7	8	**9**
10	11	**12**	13	14	**15**	16	17	**18**
19	20	**21**	22	23	**24**	25	26	**27**
28	29	**30**	31	32	**33**	34	35	**36**
37	38	**39**	40	41	**42**	43	44	**45**
46	47	**48**	49	50	**51**	52	53	**54**
55	56	**57**	58	59	**60**	61	62	**63**

1	2	**3**	4	5	**6**	7	8
9	10	11	**12**	13	14	**15**	16
17	**18**	19	20	**21**	22	23	**24**
25	26	**27**	28	29	**30**	31	32
33	34	35	**36**	37	38	**39**	40
41	**42**	43	44	**45**	46	47	**48**
49	50	**51**	52	53	**54**	55	56
57	58	59	**60**	61	62	**63**	64

1	2	**3**	4	5	**6**
7	8	**9**	10	11	**12**
13	14	**15**	16	17	**18**
19	20	**21**	22	23	**24**
25	26	**27**	28	29	**30**
31	32	**33**	34	35	**36**
37	38	**39**	40	41	**42**
43	44	**45**	46	47	**48**
49	50	**51**	52	53	**54**
55	56	**57**	58	59	**60**

N.B. 6 and 9 can be divided exactly by 3, so the grids which are 6 squares wide and 9 squares wide, are shaded in vertical straight lines.

FLOWER BEDS (page 21)
Tanya ran the furthest.

WHO HAS MOST? (pages 34 & 35)
The mice with the most are Robert, Richard, Sandeep and Daniel.

MORE STORIES (pages 36 & 37)

(1) 24 legs (2) 4 hours (3) Shaun – he is oldest because

he was born first. (4) 7 biscuits each (5) 4 years older

(6) 8 pieces.

HIDING (pages 38 & 39)
Emma Mouse is behind bush 1.

WHAT COMES NEXT? (pages 40 & 41)

(1) 11,13,15 (2) 16,14,12 (3) 28,35,42 (4) 6,10,15

(5) 18, 24, 30 (6) 45,40,35 (7) 16,18,20 (8) 12, 9, 6

(9) 7, 6, 5.

TABLES RACE (2) (page 44)

(1) 12	(6) 36	(11) 8	(16) 18
(2) 6	(7) 0	(12) 35	(17) 80
(3) 30	(8) 40	(13) 0	(18) 3
(4) 12	(9) 30	(14) 20	(19) 0
(5) 0	(10) 10	(15) 0	(20) 35.

CLOCK SHOP (page 45)

(1) Right (2) Wrong (3) Right (4) Wrong

(5) Wrong – the big hand and the little hand are wrong!

(6) Wrong (7) Right.

MOUSE NESTS (pages 46 & 47)

How many mice liked paper best?	4
How many mice liked leaves best?	2
How many mice liked hay best?	3
How many mice liked cloth best?	7
	16

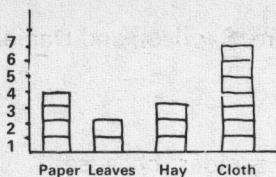

Most mice liked *cloth* the best.

CARD CODE (pages 48 & 49)

What is grey and has four legs and a trunk?

A mouse going on holiday.

MOUSE IN A MUDDLE (page 50)

$4 \times 6 = 24$
$6 \times 5 = 30$
$6 \times 6 = 36$
$12 \div 6 = 2$
$6 \times 0 = 0$
$18 \div 6 = 3$
$6 \times 1 = 6.$

CHECK YOUR SPELLING (page 52)

1. one
2. two
3. three
4. four
5. five
6. six
7. seven
8. eight
9. nine
10. ten
20. twenty
30. thirty
40. forty
50. fifty
60. sixty
70. seventy
80. eighty
90. ninety
100. hundred.

CROSSWORD (page 53)

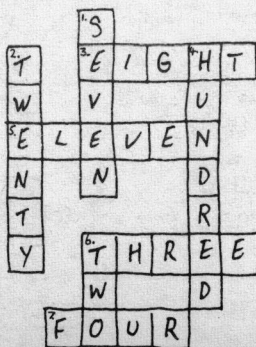

PIE QUESTIONS (pages 54 & 55)
1. Sam 2. Alice 3. Bella 4. Patrick 5. Jamie 6. Lily.

NIBBLED NUMBERS (pages 56 & 57)
Amy Mouse's nibbled number is 4.
Jo Mouse's nibbled number is 9.

TICK OR CROSS (pages 58 & 59)
Mouse got 6 wrong.

The answers should have been these:
$2 \times 3 = 6$; $6 \times 3 = 18$; $9 \times 3 = 27$;
$2 \times 5 = 10$; $6 \times 5 = 30$; $7 \times 5 = 35$.

MORE SANDWICHES (page 60)

(1) Halves (2) Quarters (3) Quarters (4) Halves.

Here is another way of cutting sandwiches into quarters:

ADD-UPS (pages 62 & 63)
If you found at least 5 groups on each square, well done!

If you found more than 10 groups on each square – excellent!

FROG HOPS (pages 64 & 65)

Frog visited me – Mouse.

DOTTY SHAPES (pages 66 & 67)

(A) hexagon (B) pentagon

(C) pentagon (D) hexagon

(E) pentagon.

QUESTION MACHINE (pages 68 & 69)

Here are some questions which make 9:
3×3; $2 + 7$; $4 + 5$; $6 + 3$; $1 + 8$; $9 + 0$.
You might have thought of other ones, too!

Here are some questions which make 12:
3×4; 2×6; 1×12; $10 + 2$; $9 + 3$;
$8 + 4$; $7 + 5$; $6 + 6$. Did you think of any others?

SHADY SQUARES (pages 70 & 71)
Mouse is saying "HELP!"

FAT CAT (pages 72 & 73)
Tuesday: 4 mice. Wednesday: **6 mice.** Thursday: 5 mice.

WASHING LINES (pages 74 & 75)

(a) 18 — because it is not a multiple of 10.

(b) 7 — because it is not an even number.

(c) 17 — because it is not a multiple of 3.

(d) 24 — because it is not a multiple of 5.

(e) 17 — because it is not a multiple of 4.

SHAPES CROSSWORD
(pages 76 & 77)

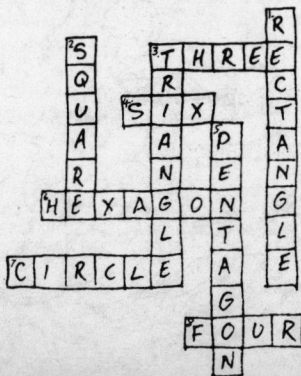

93

MIXED-UP NUMBERS (page 78)
one, twenty, six, ten, eight, two.

GARDEN PATHS (page 79)
Ashley ran the furthest.

TABLES RACE ③ (page 80)

① 8   ⑥ 100   ⑪ 16   ⑯ 24

② 25   ⑦ 18   ⑫ 21   ⑰ 5

③ 10   ⑧ 0   ⑬ 50   ⑱ 40

④ 8   ⑨ 12   ⑭ 9   ⑲ 15

⑤ 0   ⑩ 18   ⑮ 0   ⑳ 1.

SUM SEARCH (page 81)
If you found less than 10 sums: keep looking!
If you found more than 10: well done!
If you found more than 20: excellent!

PLAYGROUND (pages 82 & 83)
Monday: clockwise. Tuesday: clockwise.
Wednesday: anti-clockwise. Thursday: anti-clockwise.

TIMES TABLES CODE (pages 84 & 85)
What's the difference between an
elephant and a biscuit?
You can't dip an elephant in your tea.

DIVIDING (page 87)

① 4

② 1

③ 10

④ 0.